Hide-and-seek

Finding Hidden Shapes

by Lynn Maslen Kertell
pictures by Sue Hendra and John R. Maslen

Scholastic Inc.
New York • Toronto • London • Auckland • Sydney • Mexico City • New Delhi • Hong Kong • Buenos Aires

Seth, Tanner, and Sally were
best friends. They liked
to play hide-and-seek.

"I'm It! I'm It!" shouted Sally.
Tanner and Seth ran to hide.

"Where is Seth? Where is he?"
thought Sally. She looked and looked.

"Can't find me," called Seth.

"Where is Tanner? Where is he?"
asked Sally and Seth.

They looked and looked.
"Come and get me," teased Tanner.

"My turn to hide!" said Sally.
"Where is Sally? Where is she?"
wondered Seth and Tanner.

"Here I am," laughed Sally.

Sally, Seth, and Tanner all hid.

Where did they go?

Here they are!